MEDICINE AND MORALS

CHARLES E. CURRAN

Corpus Papers
CORPUS BOOKS: Washington/Cleveland

Medicine and Morals included in CORPUS PAPERS, a series of informative studies on specific contemporary issues in Scripture, Doctrine, Morality, and Counseling.

Corpus Papers

Raymond E. Brown and P. Joseph Cahill, *Biblical Tendencies Today: An Introduction to the Post-Bultmannians*

Avery Dulles, *Myth, Biblical Revelation, and Christ*

John R. Cavanagh, *Sexual Anomalies and Counseling*

Albert R. Jonsen, *Patterns in Moral Behavior*

Charles P. Kindregan, *Abortion, the Law, and Defective Children*

Robert P. O'Neil and Michael A. Donovan, *Children and Sin*

Anthony T. Padovano, *Original Sin and Christian Anthropology*

Peter J. Riga, *Sexuality and Marriage in Recent Catholic Thought*

Robert H. Springer, *Conscience and the Behavioral Sciences*

Jules Toner, *What Is Love?*

Frederick C. Copleston, *Man and Meaning*

Robert North, *In Search of the Human Jesus*

Thomas F. O'Meara, *The Presence of the Spirit of God*

Daniel Maguire, *Moral Absolutes and the Magisterium*

Richard McSorley, *Kill For Peace?*

Francis J. Buckley, *Children and God*

John McLaughlin, *Love Before Marriage*

Contents

General Introduction

Renewal and aggiornamento characterize contemporary Roman Catholic life and theology. In the area of theology, the scientific study of the Scriptures has been most drastically affected by renewal. Biblical scholars and exegetes have employed the auxiliary sciences to come to a better understanding of the Word of God in the words of men. Form criticism, literary genre, midrash, and myth are now commonly employed tools in Roman Catholic scriptural study. In fact, it is improper even to speak of Roman Catholic scriptural study, since scriptural study is now truly ecumenical.

Dogmatic or systematic theology is also experiencing the currents of renewal. The insights of modern scientific findings together with a better understanding of the Scriptures have brought Catholic theologians to see the cultural and historical accretions which have become a part of our theological heritage. The teaching on original sin serves as an excellent example. Scripture studies confirm the non-historical character of the Genesis account of original sin; evolutionary theories cast doubt on monogenism; the influence of a classical worldview is present in the teaching on the handing down of original sin. Theologians today are struggling with the problem of original sin in terms of the sin of the world.

Less than a few decades ago, a more rationalistic approach argued that man could know and demonstrate the existence of God from reason. Now theologians realize the embarrasing inadequacies of a one-sided rationalistic apologetics. Contemporary Catholic theologians are also calling into question the real existence of angels and even devils. Theology has previously maintained that faith is a firm and certain assent, but modern theologians speak of faith existing side by side with unbelief in the same person. An older theology stressed divine providence; today theology speaks to men come of age in terms of responsibility. Contemporary theology admits the ecclesial realities of other Christian Churches. All these changes and others have brought to the forefront the important question of the development of doctrine. Advances in man's knowledge of history, culture, philosophy, anthropology, and the empirical sciences have all played a part in such change and development.

Moral theology, or Christian ethics, can be no exception to the theological renewal in the Church. The same factors that are operative in the area of Scripture and dogmatic theology are also operative in the area of moral theology. In fact, one should expect greater change and development in the area of moral theology, since moral theology deals with man and his actions. In the last two or three centuries our understanding of man and his world has dramatically changed. The industrial, scientific, democratic, and educational revolutions have all taken place. Unfortunately, all the changes in man's understanding of himself and his world have had little or no effect as yet on Catholic moral theology.

A call for change and development does not imply a disrespect of tradition and what has gone before. A proper attitude toward tradition and previous teachings avoids the opposite extremes of either canonizing the past or forgetting about the past. A non-historical approach frequently forgets that a previous teaching was deeply affected by the historical and cultural circumstances in which it arose.

The developing Catholic teaching on religious liberty and on the separation of Church and State serves as a good illustration. The union of Church and State was proposed as an ideal. However, a difficulty arose because in certain countries it was impossible to have a union of Church and State. Theologians conceived the distinction between thesis and hypothesis. The thesis or the "ideal" calls for union, but in practice the opposite may be tolerated. Bishop Dupanloup of Orleans wrote a pamphlet after Pope Pius IX's encyclical *Quanta Cura* and the *Syllabus* in which he mitigated the harshness of the papal teaching by employing a distinction between thesis and hypothesis. The distinction itself finally appears in the documents of the papal magisterium only with Leo XIII, the successor of Pius IX. However, Vatican Council II accepted the fact that the distinction between thesis and hypothesis did not really do justice to the question of Church and State and religious liberty. Today no Catholic theologian would uphold the union of Church and State as an ideal toward which all Catholics must strive. History has taught us that the "ideal" was really not an abstract ideal at all, but rather the canonization of a particular historical manifestation. The "ideal" was greatly influenced by the cultural and historical conditions of the time. (In somewhat the same way the universal condemnation of usury canonized and absolutized a concept of money that was historically conditioned.)

A theologian sins against a proper understanding of history and tradition if he merely repeats formulae and conclusions from the past and completely forgets the different historical and cultural settings in which such conclusions were formed. Theology remains true to the past and to the present when it tries to interpret the present and the future in the light of the past. Good theology avoids the opposite extreme of paying no attention to the past. A proper understanding of Christian experience and teaching in the past enables the theologian to interpret the present better and to avoid the absolutizing of any moment in history–either past or present.

Catholic theology in general and moral theology in particular have not kept pace with the revolutions which have characterized man's understanding of himself and the world in which he lives. A historical overview of moral theology will help to explain the gap between moral theology and modern man's understanding of himself and his world.

Since the sixteenth and seventeenth centuries moral theology has undergone very little change either in the structure or in the content of the manuals of moral theology. After the sixteenth century, moral theology became very practically oriented and lost contact with both dogmatic theology and philosophy. Speculative theology and philosophy among Catholics were themselves in a poor state because of the nominalistic and positivistic approach of the times. Moral theology became more aligned with canon law than the more speculative sciences. But practical reasons were primary in diverting the attention of moral theology to the narrow and practical scope of training confessors for the sacrament of penance.

The historical needs of the Church have often been influential in determining the shape of moral theology. The general introduction of private penance in the sixth century gave rise to the penitentials, books which indicated the precise penances to be assigned for particular sins. In the twelfth century a new genre appeared, the *Summae Confessorum*. The insistence on yearly participation in the sacrament of penance by the Fourth Lateran Council encouraged the formation of this type of penitential handbook containing the necessary moral and canonical information for the confessor. The *Summae* evolved through the fifteenth century into the alphabetical *Summae* which abandoned any attempt at a logical and speculative explanation of the material and just listed and explained the necessary items according to alphabetical order. However, the more theoretical and speculative aspects of moral theology or ethics were still retained in the universities.

One of the aims of the Council of Trent was to provide a better training for candidates for the priesthood. The minor clergy were in no way adequately prepared for their ministry. Most of the lower clergy could never attend the protracted university course of fourteen years which led to the doctorate in theology. Also a number of abuses had contributed to the inadequate training of the lower clergy. The Council of Trent again called for a renewal of the sacrament of penance and legislated the necessity of yearly confession. The Society of Jesus was quick to carry out the reforms intended by Trent, especially in the renewal of the sacrament of penance. According to the Jesuit *Ratio Studiorum* of 1586, the candidates for the priesthood were to be given a two-year course which would properly prepare them for their priestly ministry in the confessional. The approach was very practical and pastoral. The first-year course contained tracts on human acts, conscience, laws, sins, and all the commandments except the seventh. The second-year curriculum included the seventh commandment (especially contracts), the sacraments, censures, the duties and obligations of the various states of life. The *Institutiones Theologiae Moralis* were textbooks based on the plan of the *Ratio Studiorum*.

The manuals of theology which were seminary classroom fare until just a few years ago follow the same structure and contain almost the same content as the seventeenth-century *Institutiones*. The references to anything happening in other areas of Catholic thinking or to "secular" thinking are very conspicuous by their absence. The manuals merely added the various encyclicals and directives issued by the hierarchical magisterium. The most widely used manuals of moral theology were written in "the Jesuit tradition." However, the textbooks in the Dominican school had the same practical orientation, although there was a more speculative approach on some issues. In nineteenth-century Germany, moral theologians began to widen the scope of moral theology to embrace a consideration of the whole Christian life. The newer German manuals of moral theology did not really have much effect outside Germany until the appearance of Bernard Haring's *The Law of Christ* in the 1950s and 1960s.

The very practical scope of moral theology was not the only factor that isolated such theology from other intellectual currents of thought. All Roman Catholic theology was isolated from the philosophical and empirical insights developed since the seventeenth century. The great revolutions in man's understanding of himself and his world had little or no effect upon Catholic thinking until recently. Ever since the Reformation, Roman Catholic life and theology have tended to exist in a ghetto and react defensively to any of the advances of the time. The Reformation, the Enlightenment, and scientific advances were looked upon as threats to Catholic belief and teachings. The Catholic Church in general opted for a position of intransigence and opposition to the thinking of the modern world.

The nineteenth century witnessed the confrontation between the Church and the modern world. Would Catholic thought make any accommodation to the stirrings in the modern world or would it rigidly refuse any accommodation? The confrontation centered especially on the question of liberalism and the freedoms advocated by the spirit of the revolution in France. The liberal and secular thinkers advocated freedom of religion, freedom of speech, freedom of the press, and freedom of intellectual inquiry. There were definitely unacceptable aspects to the liberalism and the thinking of the nineteenth century, but the general attitude of the Church was a rigid condemnation rather than an attempt to purify and assimilate the acceptable parts of the thinking of the age. Catholics themselves were divided on the approach to the contemporary world, but the intransigent attitude finally emerged as the offical policy. In France and Belgium "Catholic liberals" supported the notion of seperation of Church and State and religious liberty–a free Church in a free State according to the dictum of Montalembert. In Italy the liberalism of the day assumed primarily a political stance in working for the unification of Italy and the elimination of the Papal States.

In Germany the primary area of conflict was more in the call by some Catholic thinkers for an accommodation with the thinking of the modern world. A congress of Catholic intellectuals was convened in Munich in 1863 to bring Catholic thinking abreast of the best thinking of the day. However, the reaction of Rome was negative. The general Roman reaction was to oppose rigidly all accommodation and to call for a return and renewal of the theology and philosophy of St. Thomas. In the light of this historical background, one can better understand the meaning and importance of Leo XIII's encyclical *Aeterni Patris* (1879), in which the pope called for the revival of Thomism in Catholic schools and seminaries. The directives imposing Thomism increased with the years. The Code of Canon Law which went into effect in 1918 states that philosophy and theology in Catholic schools and seminaries are to be taught *"ad Angelici Doctoris rationem, doctrinam, et principia . . ."* (Canon 1366, §2). In this manner Catholic philosophy and theology were supposed to be insulated from much of the dangerous thinking of the day. The twentieth-century revival of Thomism had little effect on the manuals of moral theology because of their practical scope and isolation from dogma and theology. However, the exclusive emphasis on Thomistic theology and philosophy prevented any possible dialogue of moral theology with contemporary thought.

This brief historical overview shows the need for a renewal in moral theology. Interestingly, the nineteenth-century opposition to the modern world in the form of opposition to religious liberty and unification of Italy has already ceased. However, moral theology has not undergone a renewal through contact and dialogue with modern man's understanding of himself. The renewal in moral theology in the last few years has been through the scriptural and liturgical renewals. Such a renewal has been most beneficial in trying to indicate the true vocation of the Christian constantly striving for the reign of God. But the process of renewal now calls for a dialogue with modern philosophical thought, with the natural and social sciences, contemporary human experience and man's understanding of himself in the modern world. The *Pastoral Constitution on the Church in the Modern World* has recognized the great changes that have occurred in man's understanding of himself and the world (n. 44). The last three centuries have seen revolutionary changes in science, technology, and knowledge. The world and the Church have also recognized the dignity of man and his need for freedom and liberty to live as a responsible person in the modern world. Moral theology is just beginning such a dialogue.

MEDICINE AND MORALS

CHARLES E. CURRAN

The natural law has recently become a very important topic of discussion in moral theology. The ecumenical dialogue has forced Roman Catholic theologians to re-examine this theory. Many Protestant theologians point out that the natural law concept constitutes a primary source of disagreement between Protestant and Catholic ethicians.[1] The ongoing dialogue with our world has shown Catholic theologians a world and a reality that differs considerably from the view of the world and reality enshrined in the traditional textbook understanding of natural law.

The entire process of renewal within the Church demands a critical appraisal of natural law theory. The debate over contraception, for example, has evolved into a questioning of natural law itself, as a rethinking of contraception necessarily entailed a critique of the natural law system on which it was based. But to make a definitive critique of the natural law here is impossible. The aims of this study are more modest: it will consider the concept of natural law which underlies Catholic moral teaching on medical morals.

Medical ethics has occupied a prominent place in Catholic moral theology in the present century. In the United States alone, a proportionately large number of books has been written recently in this area.[2] Furthermore, many of the utterances of recent popes have been concerned with the moral problems confronting modern medicine.[3] Both the papal teaching and the textbooks base their medical morality upon natural law. Thus, medical morality serves as a good illustration of the use of natural law in Catholic moral theology. This essay will also try to show that the area of medical morality tends to show up the shortcomings in the textbook theory of natural law. (In other areas, such as social problems, where Catholic teaching has employed the concept of natural law, it has received wide-based support from many men of good will.)

POINTS OF DISSATISFACTION

There is dissatisfaction among Catholic theologians concerning a number of questions involving medical morality. Contraception comes to mind as the most obvious example. The majority report of the papal commission which examined the problem of contraception rejected the natural law arguments against contraception.[4] Even many who have upheld the ban against contraception reasserted by Paul VI in *Humanae Vitae,* admit that the natural law arguments are not convincing.[5] However, there are also other applications of natural law theory in the area of medicine which do not command universal assent from contemporary Catholic theologians.

Contraception and Sterilization. Logically, the question of sterilization is closely connected with contraception. Catholic theologians have generally proposed that direct sterilization (either temporary or permanent) is immoral. Sterilization is permitted only if it is indirect; that is, "if a pathological condition of the organ renders it necessary for the preservation of the patient's life or health."[6]

Traditionally, theologians have distinguished contraception from sterilization by the fact that contraception interferes with the sexual act, whereas sterilization interferes with the sexual faculty itself.[7] (According to this theological terminology, the anovulant pills involve sterilization and not contraception.[8]) Once a theologian admits that man may interfere in the reproductive process, there is no essential difference (other than the permanency of the effect) between interfering with the act of sexual intercourse (contraception) or interfering with the reproductive faculty (anovulant pills, sterilizing operations).

Interestingly enough, at one time a few Catholic theologians were willing to admit the liceity of the anovulant pill (a sterilization) and still deny the morality of contraceptive intercourse.[9] But the significant moral difference between sterilization and contraception is the fact that sterilization, especially through surgical procedures, tends to be more permanent than contraception.

Medicine itself has always maintained the principle of economy: man should interfere only to the extent that it is necessary. For example, medicine prefers to avoid surgery if other means of treatment are sufficient. Likewise, a permanent procedure should not be employed when a temporary procedure would be sufficient. The principle of economy also has moral validity. However, there are occasions when a permanent sterilization is called for, especially in those cases in which the woman can never again bear children. Thus, a change in contraception points toward a change in the condemnation of direct sterilization.

Artificial Insemination. There are other instances of dissatisfaction with textbook solutions to moral problems in the area of medicine. "The Ethical and Religious Directives for Catholic Hospitals," sanctioned by the Catholic Hospital Association of the United States and Canada, maintains: "Sterility tests involving the procurement of the male specimen by masturbation . . . are morally objectionable" (n. 38).[10] A partial reason for the condemnation is given in an earlier directive. "The unnatural use of the sex faculty (for example, masturbation) is never permitted even for a laudable purpose" (n. 29). Pope Pius XII spoke in the same vein.[11] However, contemporary theologians have not been convinced that such an action is wrong.[12]

In the past theology has perhaps tended to look at the action only from the physical and biological viewpoint. Masturbation was totally defined by its physiological properties. However, human understanding tells us there is quite a difference between masturbation and the ejaculation of semen to obtain a specimen for sterility tests. The human act seems to be the obtaining of semen for examination and not the human act of masturbation. The whole purpose and intent of the person gives a different meaning to the action. To describe the morality of an action solely in terms of the physical nature of the faculty apart from any other existing relationships and circumstances appears to be inadequate.

The basic question is whether artificial insemination is wrong when the wife is inseminated with her husband's semen. Pope Pius XII taught that such artificial insemination is wrong because the act of intercourse must always be a personal action which is expressive of love.[13] Some theologians, before the papal allocutions, thought that an absolute condemnation of artificial insemination puts too much emphasis on the individual physical action as such.[14] Ordinarily the conception process begins by the depositing of male semen in the vagina of the woman through physical intercourse. However, occasionally it may happen that such normal intercourse does not provide good conditions for conception to occur. By bypassing the normal way of insemination, science can provide a better possibility for the husband's seed to fertilize his wife's ovum. It is true that insemination must take place within the context of a relationship of marital love; but the physical act of natural intercourse does not seem to be of absolute and determining moral necessity.

A concrete case illustrates the difficulties inherent in the present ban on artificial insemination in the medical moral textbooks. John is a handicapped person suffering from a partial paralysis in the legs. John is able to have sexual intercourse with his wife, but real penetration is often not attained. Yet John and Alice desperately want a family. A sympathetic Catholic doctor tried to help. After having relations with her husband, Alice rushed to the doctor's office hoping that she still retained some of the semen. The doctor then tried to gather whatever semen was still in the vagina in a syringe, and then insert the semen into the cervix, thus avoiding the harmful acids of the vagina. Such an approach did not result in a pregnancy. Then the doctor decided that John and Alice should have sexual relations in his private office. The doctor would enter immediately after intercourse and be able to gather what little semen there might be in the vagina before the harmful vaginal fluids could affect the semen.

The natural human reaction rejects such a solution as inhuman. Even though conception would then occur after a "natural act," the entire circumstances of such marital intercourse seem unnatural. To obtain the husband's semen in such a case, by voluntary ejaculation which is then medically inserted into the cervix of the wife, does not seem to be an immoral procedure.

The Double Effect. There has also been discussion in recent years about the principle of the double effect.[15] The principle of double effect has bearing on the questions of direct killing, direct abortion, direct mutilation, and direct sterilization. The principle tries to come to grips with those complex human situations where both good and evil exist intertwined. If the evil effect is only permitted (and not directly intended), then the evil effect can be permitted for a proportionate reason. The Directives of the Catholic Hospital Association, for example, describe direct killing as a procedure "whose sole immediate effect" is the death of a human being (n. 12).

In this sense the sole immediate effect of an action is determined by the physical structure of the action itself, without any consideration of the other values present in the situation. The question of ectopic pregnancy serves as a good illustration. Within the framework of the principle of double effect, the sole immediate effect of the action cannot be thought of as the abortion itself. The immediate effect of the action has to be the curing of some pathological condition. Earlier theologians maintained that an ectopic pregnancy (generally a fetus in the tube) could not be removed unless the tube itself had ruptured.

Once the tube had ruptured, it was in a pathological condition and could be removed even though it contained a fetus.

Lately, some theologians have maintained that the doctor does not have to wait for the tube to rupture. The blood of the tube is already being infected by the fetus and is thus pathological before the rupture occurs. Thus one may remove the tube with the fetus in it even before the tube ruptures.[16]

But here a further question must also be raised. What if the doctor can interfere by removing the fetus without taking out the tube? If the doctor has to remove the tube too, then the chances of the woman's giving birth again are greatly reduced. By removing just the fetus, the doctor does not impair the child-bearing ability of the mother. The doctor knows that the fetus has no chance to live and sooner or later will have to be removed. The logical solution would be to remove the fetus and save the tube, if possible. Such a solution appears to be very moral, but the usual application of the theory of direct killing or direct abortion would not admit the liceity of such a procedure.

The identification of the direct effect by the sole immediate effect of the action has caused some Catholic theologians to question such an understanding of "direct." "An act may or may not be abortion as a human act although materially and externally it is nevertheless exactly the same act."[17] Theologians are quick to point out the problems created by the notion of direct mutilation defined in terms of the physical structure of the act itself. For this reason, many theologians originally condemned transplantation of organs as a direct mutilation. To transplant an organ from one person to another, the organ obviously must be removed from the first person. However, an act whose sole immediate effect is the removal of an eye or a kidney involves a direct mutilation. The fact that it is later to be given to a person in great need of such an organ does not change the fact that the sole immediate effect of the action is mutilation.[18]

Archbishop Denis Hurley has proposed a somewhat different principle to apply in some complex situations where both good and evil effects exist. Hurley speaks of the principle of the overriding right, and hesitatingly mentions the possibility of employing such a principle in the case of abortion when the mother's right to life is put in jeopardy by the fetus.[19] The principle of the overriding right, if logically extended, could apply to a number of other situations, even in the area of abortion. Hurley's principle does not rely on a moral determination based on the sole immediate effect of the action, but rather tries to weigh the different moral values at stake in the concrete situation.[20]

Medical Experimentation. Catholic moral teaching has not been favorable to medical experimentation. The certitude with which some actions were proposed as immoral (if it had not been widely ignored) would have prevented much profitable medical experimentation. Transplantation of organs is just one example. Many tests on human sperm would have been condemned because the sperm was held to be obtained through immoral means. A rigid belief in the absolute certitude of the immorality of medical procedures makes experimentation and medical progress most difficult for Catholic scientists. In the future Catholic theologians should be wary of insisting that some actions are certainly and always immoral.

The dissatisfaction with a number of conclusions in recent Catholic understanding of medical morals has been sufficiently documented. But present tensions in medical morality are nothing compared to those that will occur in trying to solve some of the genetic problems of the future. The individual problems, of course, are symptomatic of the underlying difficulties with the system, or theory, of natural law upon which such conclusions are based. (This essay assumes that the reader is generally familiar with the theory of natural law found in the applications to medical problems in Catholic moral textbooks.) A general understanding of Catholic medical moral teaching together with the dissatisfactions mentioned point to some of the difficulties involved in such a system.

The main problem stems from the too easy identification

of the physical action itself, or the physical structure of the effects, with the moral determination of the human action. The human action cannot be judged merely in and by itself or according to its own physical structure alone, with no consideration given to the other values present in the situation. Also, the certitude with which Catholic theologians have maintained that some actions are always wrong in the area of medical morals, and the current call for change in these areas, makes one wary of any system which continues to profess such certitude.

Historical investigation will partially explain how such questionable ways of viewing morality have entered into the system of Catholic medical morality and can suggest ways for avoiding such apparent distortions in the future. By reviewing at least some of the historical antecedents of these questionable teachings in medical morals, a way may be found to avoid such distortions in the future.

NATURAL IDENTIFIED WITH PHYSICAL: ULPIAN

The danger that arises if we identify the moral action simply with the biological and physical structure of the human act is evident in the controversy over contraception and sterilization. The notion of "direct" in the principle of double effect also seems to be too closely tied both to the physical structure of the human act and the sole immediate physical effect of that action.

Ethical theory constantly vacillates between two polarities —naturalism and idealism. Naturalism sees man in perfect continuity with the nature about him. Nature shapes and even determines man. Idealism views man completely apart from nature and sees man as completely surpassing nature. Even Thomistic philosophy, the main Catholic proponent of natural law theory, knows an ambivalence between nature and reason.

The Thomistic natural law concept vacillates at times between the order of nature and the order of reason.[21] The general Thomistic thrust is towards the predominance of reason in natural law theory. However, there is in Thomas a definite tendency to identify the demands of natural law with physical and biological processes. Thomas, too, is a historical person conditioned by the circumstances and influences of his own time. These influences help explain the tendency (but not the predominant tendency) in Thomas to identify the human action with the physical and biological structure of the human act. A major one is Ulpian, a Roman lawyer who died in 228.

Ulpian and Thomas. Ulpian defined the natural law as that which nature teaches all the animals. Ulpian distinguished the natural law from the *ius gentium*. The *ius naturale* is that which is common to all animals, whereas the *ius gentium* is that which is proper to men.[22] Albert the Great rejected Ulpian's definition of the natural law, but Thomas accepted it, and even showed a preference for such a definition.[23] In the *Commentary on the Sentences,* for example, Thomas maintains that the most strict definition of natural law is the one proposed by Ulpian: *ius naturae est quod natura omnia animalia docuit.*[24]

In his *Commentary on the Nicomachean Ethics,* Thomas again shows a preference for Ulpian's definition. Aristotle had proposed a twofold division of *iustum naturale* and *iustum legale,* but Ulpian proposed the threefold distinction of *ius naturale, ius gentium* and *ius civile.* Thomas solves the apparent dilemma by saying that the Roman law concepts of *ius naturale* and *ius gentium* both belong under the Aristotelian category of *iustum naturale.* Man has a double nature. The *ius naturale* rules that which is proper to both man and the animals, such as the union of the sexes and the education of offspring; whereas the *ius gentium* governs the rational part of man which is proper to man alone, and embraces such things as fidelity to contracts.[25]

In the *Summa Theologiae* Thomas cites Ulpian's definition on a number of occasions.[26] In the classification of natural law again Thomas shows a preference for Ulpian's definition. Thomas accepts the division proposed by Isidore of Seville, according to which the *ius gentium* belongs to the category of human law and not to the category of divine law. Thomas uses Ulpian's definition to explain Isidore's division. The natural law pertains to the divine law because it is common to man and to all the animals.[27] In a sense, the *ius gentium* does pertain to the category of human law because man uses his reason to deduce the conclusions of the *ius gentium*.

Thomas thus employs Ulpian's definition of natural law as opposed to what reason deduces (the *ius gentium*) to defend the division of law proposed by Isidore. The same question receives somewhat the same treatment later in the *Summa*.[28] The texts definitely show that Thomas knew and even accepted the definition of natural law proposed by Ulpian.

Ulpian's Concept of Natural Law. Ulpian is important for the understanding of natural law morality. The natural law for Ulpian is defined in terms of those actions which are common to man and all the animals. There results from this the definite danger of identifying the human action with a mere animal or biological process. "Nature" and "natural" in Ulpian's meaning are distinguished from that which is specifically human and derived by reason. Traditional theology has in the past definitely employed the words "natural" and "nature" as synonymous with animal or biological processes and not as denoting human actions in accord with the rational nature of man.

Moral theology textbooks even speak of sins according to nature. The manuals generally divide the sins against the sixth commandment into two categories—the sins against nature (*peccata contra naturam*) and sins in accord with nature (*peccata secundum naturam*). "Nature" is thus used in Ulpian's sense, as that which is common to man and all the animals. In matters of sexuality (and Ulpian himself uses the example of the sexual union as an illustration of the natural law), man shares with the animal world the fact of the sexual union whereby male seed is deposited in the vas of the female. Sins against nature, therefore, are those acts in which the animal or biological process is not observed—pollution, sodomy, bestiality, and contraception. Sins according to nature are those acts in which the proper biological process is observed but something is lacking in the sphere which belongs only to rational men. These include fornication, adultery, incest, rape, and sacrilege.[29]

The classification of sins against chastity furnishes concrete proof that "nature" has been used in Catholic theology to refer to animal processes without any intervention of human reason. Many theologians have rightly criticized the approach to marriage sexuality used by Catholic natural law theoreticians because such an approach concentrated primarily on the biological components of the act of intercourse. The personal aspects of the sexual union received comparatively scant attention in many of the manuals of moral theology. Ulpian's influence has made it easier for Catholic natural law thinking to identify the human act simply with the physical structure of the act.

Ulpian's Anthropology. Ulpian's understanding of the natural law logically leads to disastrous consequences in the anthropological understanding of man. The distinction between two parts in man—that which is common to man and all the animals, and that which is proper to man—results in a two-layer version of man. A top layer of rationality is merely added to an already constituted bottom layer of animality. The union between the two layers is merely extrinsic—the one lies on top of the other. The animal layer retains its own finalities and tendencies, independent of the demands of rationality. Thus man may not interfere in the animal processes and finalities. Note that the results of such an anthropology are most evident in the area of sexuality.

A proper understanding of man should start with that which is proper to man. Rationality does not just lie on top of animality, but rationality characterizes and guides the whole person. Animal processes and finalities are not untouchable. Man's whole vocation, we have come to see, is to bring order and intelligence into the world, and to shape animal and biological finalities toward a truly human purpose. Ulpian's concept of natural law logically falsifies the understanding of man and tends to canonize the finalities and processes which man shares with the animal world.

A better anthropology would see the distinctive in man as guiding and directing the totality of his being. For Thomas rationality constituted what is distinctive and characteristic in man. Modern philosophers differ from Thomas on what is distinctively human. Phenomenologists tend to view man as a symbolic person; while personalists look upon man as an incarnate spirit, a "thou" in relation to other "you's." However, all would agree in rejecting a notion of man that sees animality existing in man and that retains animal finalities and tendencies without any intervention of the specifically human part of man.

I am not asserting that Thomas always identified human actions with animal processes or the physical structure of the act. In fact, the general outlines of the hylomorphic theory, by speaking of material and formal components of reality, try to avoid any physicism or biologism. Nevertheless, the adoption of Ulpian's understanding of "nature" and "natural" logically leads to the identification of the human act itself with animal processes and with the mere physical structure of the act. Such a distorted view of the human act becomes especially prevalent in the area of medical morals, for in medical morality one can more easily conceive a moral human action solely in terms of the physical structure of that action.

Likewise, Ulpian's notion of nature easily leads to a morality based on the finality of a faculty independently of any considerations of the total human person or the total human community. One must, of course, avoid the opposite danger of paying no attention to the physical structure of the act or to external actions in themselves. However, Catholic theology in the area of medical morality has suffered from an oversimple identification of the human action with an animal process or finality.

Marriage and Sexuality. Ulpian's understanding of natural law logically has had another deleterious effect on Catholic moral theology. Until the last decade magisterial pronouncements frequently spoke of the primary and secondary ends of marriage.[30] The latest statements of Pope Paul, and the Pastoral Constitution on the Church in the Modern World (*Gaudium et Spes*), happily avoid this terminology.[31] However, such a distinction has obviously influenced Catholic teaching on marriage and sexuality. Many people have questioned the distinction as being contradicted by the experience of married couples.

The distinction logically follows from Ulpian's concept of the natural law and man, although I do not claim that Ulpian is the source of such a distinction. "Primary" is that which is common to man and all the animals. Ulpian, and Thomas in citing Ulpian, use the union of the sexes and the procreation and education of offspring as examples of that which is common to man and all the animals. "Secondary" is that which is proper to man. Since only men and not animals have sexual intercourse as a sign and expression of love, the love union aspect of sexuality remains proper to man and therefore secondary. The former teaching on the ends of marriage is logically connected with Ulpian's understanding of man and natural law. Thus the teaching of Ulpian on natural law has a logical connection with the inadequate understanding of a human action as identified with an animal process.

A MORE PRIMITIVE ATTITUDE

A second and more general historical factor has also influenced the tendency to make the processes of nature inviolable. Stoic philosophy well illustrates a more general historical factor that tends to identify the human action with its physical or natural structure. One should avoid too many generalizations about the Stoics because Stoic philosophy included a number of different thinkers who covered a comparatively long span of years. In addition, Stoic philosophers invoked the natural law to justify practices that contemporary natural law theoreticians brand as immoral.[32] However, there is a common thrust to the ethical doctrine proposed by the Stoics.

Nature: Norm or Servant. Ethics considers man and his actions. Man wants to find happiness. What actions should man perform to find his happiness and fulfillment? A more primitive and less technical society will come to conclusions different from those reached by a more technically and scientifically developed society. Primitive man soon realizes that he finds his happiness in conforming himself to the patterns of nature.

Primitive man remains almost helpless when confronted with the forces of nature. The forces of nature are so strong that man is even tempted to bow down and adore. He realizes the futility in trying to fight them. His happiness will come only by adjusting himself.

Nature divides the day into light and dark. When darkness descends, there is little or nothing that man can do except sleep. When the hot sun is beating down near the equator, he will find happiness only by avoiding work and overexposure in the sun. In colder climates, man will be happy only when he uses clothing and shelter to protect himself from nature. If he wants to be happy, he will stay under some form of shelter and avoid the rain and snow. If there is a mountain in his path, the wise man will walk around the mountain rather than suffer the ardors of trying to scale the peak. For man living in a primitive society (in the sense of non-scientific and non-technical), happiness is found in conforming himself to nature.

Stoic philosophy built on this understanding of man living in a non-technical society. As Greeks, the Stoics believed in an intelligible world. They made the universe as a whole—the cosmos—their principle of intelligibility. Stoic philosophy held that reason governed the order of nature. Man's happiness consisted in conforming himself to reason, that is, in conforming himself to the order of nature. But nature was informed by reason or even identifiable with reason. The primary norm of morality, therefore, was conformity to nature.[33]

We who live in a scientific and technological society will have a different view of man and his happiness. Modern man does not find his happiness in conforming to nature. The whole ethos and genius of modern society is different. Contemporary man makes nature conform to him rather than vice-versa. Through electricity man can change night into day. There are very few things that modern man cannot do at night now that it is illuminated by electricity.

Contemporary man uses artificial heat in the winter and air conditioning in the summer to bring nature into conformity with his needs and desires. Nature did not provide man with wings to fly; in fact, the law of gravity seems to forbid man to fly. However, science has produced the jet plane and the rocket, which propel man at great speeds around the globe and even into the vast universe. When a mountain looms up as an obstacle, modern man either levels the mountain with bulldozers or tunnels under the terrain. Modern man could never tolerate a theory which equates human happiness with conformity to nature. Contemporary man interferes with the processes of nature to make nature conform to man.

These few paragraphs have not attempted to prove the influence of Stoic philosophy on St. Thomas. Rather, Stoic philosophy was used to illustrate how the conditions existing in a non-technological society will influence the philosophical understanding of man and ethics. Thomas too lived in an agrarian, non-scientific world. The non-technological worldview would be more prone to identify the human act with the physical process of nature itself.

Reality or Facticity. A more primitive society also tends to view reality in terms of the physical and the sensible. The child, unlike the adult, sees reality primarily in terms of externals. The tendency to identify the human action with the physical structure would definitely be greater in a more primitive society. For example, the importance that Catholic theology has attached to masturbatory activity, especially the overemphasis since the sixteenth century, seems to come from viewing it purely in terms of the physiological and biological aspects of the act. Modern psychology, however, does not place very great importance on such activity.

Theologians must incorporate the findings of modern science in trying to evaluate the human act of masturbation. To view it solely in terms of the physical structure of the act distorts the total reality of this human action. Contemporary theologians cannot merely repeat what older theologians have said. Today we know much more about the reality of the human act of masturbation than, say, St. Alphonsus or any other moral theologian living before the present century.[34]

It would be erroneous to say that Catholic theology has identified the human act with the brute facticity of natural processes or just the physical structure of the act itself. In the vast majority of cases, moral theology has always distinguished between the physical structure of the action and the morality of the action. The moral act of murder differs from the physical act of killing. The physical act of taking another's property does not always involve the moral act of stealing. However, in the area of medical morality (for example, contraception, sterilization, masturbation) the moral act has been considered the same as the physical structure of the act itself.

The Morality of Lying. Another area in which Catholic theologians are moving away from a description of the human act in purely physical or natural terms is lying. The contemporary theological understanding of lying serves as a salutary warning to the medical moralist because the morality of lying cannot be determined merely by examining the faculty of speech and its finality, apart from the totality of the human person speaking and the community in which he speaks.

The manuals of moral theology traditionally define lying as *locutio contra mentem.* The faculty of speech exists to express what is in the mind. When human speech does not reflect what is in the mind there is a perversion of the faculty. The perverted faculty argument is based on the finality of the faculty of speech looked at in itself. Accordingly, a lie exists when the verbal utterance does not correspond with what is in the mind. Theologians then had to face the problem created by the fact that at times the speaker simply could not speak the truth to his hearer or questioner (for example, in the case of a committed secret). A casuistry of mental reservations arose to deal with such situations.[35]

Today most contemporary Catholic theologians accept the distinction between a lie and a falsehood. A falsehood involves an untruth in the sense that the external word contradicts what is in the mind. However, the malice of lying does not consist in the perversion of the faculty of speech or the lack of conformity between the word spoken and what is in the mind. The malice of lying consists in the harm done to society and the human community through the breakdown of mutual trust and honesty. Thus, some theologians distinguish between a lie as the denial of truth which is due to the other and falsehood which is a spoken word not in conformity with what is in the mind.

The distinction between lying and falsehood obviates the rather contrived casuistry associated with broad and strict mental reservations.[36] But what does the more contemporary understanding of lying indicate? The new definition denies the validity of the perverted faculty argument. It is not sufficient merely to examine the faculty of speech and determine morality solely from the purpose of the faculty in itself. Likewise, the malice of lying does not reside in the lack of "physical" conformity between word and thought.

To view the faculty of speech apart from the total human situation of man in society seems to give a distorted view of lying. The faculty of speech must be seen and judged in a human context. Man can interfere with the physical purpose of the faculty for a higher human need and good. Perhaps in a similar vein, the notion of "direct" in the principle of the double effect cannot be judged merely from the sole immediate effect of the physical action itself, apart from the whole human context in which the act is placed. For example, if the fetus will have to be removed in the future when the tube becomes pathological, why not remove the fetus now and save the tube for future childbearing? The morality must be viewed in a total human context, and not merely judged according to the physical act itself and the natural effect of the act seen in itself apart from the whole context.

The influence of Ulpian and the view of primitive man tend to identify the total human action with the natural or biological process. A better understanding of such historically and culturally limited views of man should help the ethician in evaluating the theory of natural law as applied in the area of medical ethics. I do not claim that the summary historical evidence partially adduced here proves that the specific dissatisfactions with textbook medical morality are correct. Nor have I proved that the human act never corresponds with the physical structure of the act. However, I think it is clear that an ethician must be very cautious that older and inadequate views of man and reality do not influence his contemporary moral judgments. It does seem that the definition of Ulpian and the general views of a more primitive society have a logical connection with what seem to be erroneous conclusions in the area of medical morality. The specific disagreements with points of textbook morality in the area of medicine point to deficiencies in that theory of natural law which is the basis of medical moral ethics.

A CHANGED WORLDVIEW

A second major deficiency with the theory of natural law as applied in the area of medical morality stems from the classical worldview which is behind such a theory of natural law. Bernard Lonergan maintains that the classicist worldview has been replaced by a more historically conscious worldview.[37] In the same vein, John Courtney Murray claimed that the two different theories on Church and State represent two different methodologies and worldviews.[38] And today, other more radical Catholic thinkers are calling for a change from a substantive to a process metaphysics.[39] At the least, all these indications point to an admission by respected Catholic scholars that the so-called classical worldview has ceased to exist.

The following paragraphs will briefly sketch the differences in the two approaches to viewing reality. There are many dangers inherent in doing this. There is really no such thing as *the* classical worldview or *the* historically conscious worldview—there are many different types of historical mindedness. By arguing in favor of an historically conscious worldview, I by no means intend to endorse all the theories and opinions that might be included under such a heading.

Since this section of the essay will argue against a classical worldview, a reader might conclude that I am denying to past thinkers the possibility of any valid insights into the meaning of man and reality. Such a conclusion is far from true. There are even those (for example, Lonergan and Murray) who would argue that a moderate historically conscious methodology is in continuity with the best of Thomistic thought. We must never forget that some of the inadequacies in the classical worldview stem from the poor interpretation of St. Thomas by many of his so-called followers.

Two Views of Reality. The classicist worldview emphasizes the static, the immutable, the eternal, and the unchanging. The Greek column symbolizes this very well. There is no movement or dynamism about a Doric or Ionic column. The simple Greek column avoids all frills and baroque trimmings. The stately Greek column gives the impression of solidity, eternity, and immutability. Its majestic and sober lines emphasize an order and harmony which appear to last forever. This classical worldview speaks in terms of substances and essences. Time and history are "accidents" which do not really change the constitution of reality itself. Essences remain unchangeable and can only go through accidental changes in the course of time. Growth, dynamism, and progress therefore receive little attention.

The Platonic world of ideas well illustrates this classical worldview. Everything is essentially spelled out from all eternity. The immutable essences, the universals, exist in the world of ideas. Everything in this world of ours is a participation or an accidental modification of the subsistent ideas. Man comes to know truth and reality by abstracting from the accidents of time and place, and arriving at immutable and unchangeable essences. Such knowledge based on immutable essences is bound to attain the ultimate in certitude.

The more historically conscious worldview emphasizes the changing, developing, evolving, and historical. Time and history are more than mere accidents that do not really change essential reality. Individual and particular differences receive much more attention from a correspondingly more historically conscious methodology. The classical worldview is interested in the essence of man, which is true at all times in history and in all civilizations and circumstances. A historically minded worldview emphasizes the individual traits that characterize him. Modern man does differ quite a bit from primitive man precisely because of the historical and individual traits that he has.

In the more historical worldview the world is not static but evolving. Progress, growth, and change mark the world and all reality. Cold, chaste, objective order and harmony are not characteristic of this view. Blurring, motion, and subjective feeling are its corresponding features, as in the difference between modern art and classical art. Modern art emphasizes feeling and motion rather than harmony and balance. It is not as "objective" as classical art. The artist imposes himself and his emotions on the object.

Perhaps modern art is telling the theologian that the older distinction between the objective and the subjective is no longer completely adequate. Music also illustrates the change that has occurred in our understanding of the world and reality. Classical measure and rhythm is gone; free rhythm and feeling mean very much to the modern ear. What is meaningful music to the ear of the modern is only cacophony for the classicist. Changes in art and music illustrate the meaning of the different worldviews and also show graphically that the classical worldview is gone.

Two Methodologies. The two worldviews created two different theological methodologies. The classicist methodology tends to be abstract, *a priori,* and deductive. It wants to cut through the concrete circumstances to arrive at the abstract essence which is always true, and then works with these abstract and universal essences. In the area of moral theology, for example, the first principles of morality are established, and then other universal norms of conduct are deduced from these.

The more historical methodology tends to be concrete, *a posteriori,* and inductive. The historical approach does not brush by the accidental circumstances to arrive at the immutable essences. The concrete, the particular, and the individual are important for telling us something about reality itself. Principles are not deduced from other principles. Rather, modern man observes and experiences and then tentatively proceeds to his conclusions in a more inductive manner. Note that the historical consciousness as a methodology is an abstraction, but an abstraction or theory that tries to give more importance to particular, concrete, historical reality.

As we have noted above, John Courtney Murray claims that the different views on Church and State flow from the two different methodologies employed.[40] The older theory of the union of Church and State flows from a classicist methodology. It begins with the notion of a society. The definition of a society comes from an abstract and somewhat *a priori* notion of what such a society should be. The older theory then maintains that there are two perfect societies, and deduces their mutual duties and responsibilities, including their duties and obligations vis-à-vis one another. The theory concludes that the *cura religionis,* as it was then understood, belongs to the State. The State has the obligation of promoting the true faith.

What happens when the older theory runs headlong into a *de facto* situation in which the separation of Church and State is a historical fact? The older solution lies in a distinction between thesis and hypothesis, which roughly corresponds to the ideal order which should exist and the actual order which can be tolerated because of the presence of certain accidental historical circumstances. Notice the abstract and ahistorical characteristics of such a theory.

The newer theory of Church and State as proposed by Murray employs a more historically conscious methodology. Murray does not begin with an abstract definition of society and then deduce the obligations and rights of Church and State. Rather, Murray begins from a notion of the State derived from his observations of them in contemporary sociey. The modern State is a limited, constitutional form of government.

Its limited role contrasts with the more absolute and all-embracing role of the State in an earlier society. It does not interfere in matters that belong to the private life of individuals, such as the worship of God. Murray's theory has no need for a distinction between thesis and hypothesis, since he begins with the concrete historical reality. His conclusions then will be in harmony with the present historical situation.[41] Using a historical methodology, he can even admit that in the nineteenth century the older opinion might have been true, but in the present historical circumstances separation of Church and State is required.[42]

A classicist mentality is horrified at the thought that something could be right in one century and wrong in another. (Note, however, that the historical methodology employed by Murray and Lonergan insists on a continuity in history and rejects any atomistic existentialism which sees only the uniqueness of the present situation without any connection with what has gone before or with what will follow in history.)

A New Catholic Perspective. Theologians and philosophers are not alone in speaking of the changed perspective. In the documents of Vatican II the bishops do not officially adopt any worldview or methodology. But Vatican II definitely portrays reality in terms of a more historical worldview, and also employs a historically conscious methodology. The fact that the council has chosen to call itself a "pastoral" council is most significant; but "pastoral" must not be understood in opposition to "doctrinal." Rather, pastoral indicates a concern for the Christian faith not as truths to be learned but as a life to be lived.

The pastoral orientation of the council reflects a historical worldview. The bishops at the council also acknowledged that the Church has profited by the history and development of humanity. History reveals more about man, and opens new roads to truth. The Catholic Church must constantly engage in an exchange with the contemporary world.[43]

Gaudium et Spes frequently speaks of the need to know the signs of the times. The introductory statement of this constitution asserts the need for the Church to know them and interpret them in the light of the Gospel (n.4). The first four chapters of the first section of the constitution begin with an attempt to read the signs of the times. The attention given to what was often in the past dismissed as accidental differences of time and history shows a more historical approach to reality. The constitution does not begin with abstract and universal ideas of Church, society, state, community, and common good, but rather by scrutinizing the signs of the times. *Gaudium et Spes* thus serves as an excellent illustration of the change in emphasis in Church documents from a classicist methodology to a more historically conscious approach.

The teachings on the Church as contained in the Constitution on the Church (*Lumen Gentium*) and the other documents of Vatican II also reflect a more historical approach and understanding. Previously Catholics pictured the Church as a perfect society having all the answers, and as the one bulwark of security in a changing world. However. *Lumen Gentium* speaks often and eloquently of the pilgrim Church. The charge of triumphalism rang true in the conciliar halls of Vatican II. A pilgrim Church, however, does not pretend to have all the answers.

A pilgrim Church is ever on the march towards its goal of perfect union with Christ the spouse. A pilgrim Church is constantly striving, probing, falling, rising, and trying again. A pilgrim is one who is constantly on the road, and does not know there the security of his own home. So too the pilgrim Church is an *ecclesia semper reformanda*. Change, development, growth, struggle and tension mark the Church of Christ in this world. The notion of the pilgrim Church, even in language, differs very much from the perfect society of the theological manuals.

The conciliar documents underscore the need for the

Catholic Church to engage in dialogue—dialogue with other Christians, dialogue with Jews, dialogue with other non-Christians, dialogue with the world. Dialogue is not monologue. Dialogue presupposes that Catholics can learn from all these others. The call for dialogue supposes the historical and pilgrim nature of the Church, which does not possess all the answers but is open in the search for truth. The need for ongoing dialogue and ongoing search for truth contrast sharply with the classicist view of reality and truth.

Lumen Gentium rebuilds ecclesiology on the notion of the Church as the people of God and points out the various functions and services which exist in the Church (Chapter 2). Hierarchy is one form of service which exists in it. Another office is prohecy. The prophetic function exists independently of the hierarchy (n.12). The hierarchical Church can learn, and has learned, from the prophetic voice in the Church. History reminds us that in the Church change usually occurs from underneath. Vatican Council II brought to fruition the work of the prophets in the biblical, liturgical, catechetical, and ecumenical movements.

Thank God for Pope John and the bishops at Vatican II, we can say, but there never would have been a Vatican II if it were not for the prophets who went before. Many of them were rejected when they first proposed their teaching, but such has always been the lot of the prophet. The pilgrim Church, with the prophetic office, will always know the tension of trying to do the truth in love. The Church sorely needs to develop an older notion of the discernment of the Spirit, so that the individual himself and the total Church will be more open and ready to hear its true voice while rejecting the utterances of false prophets.[44]

The Church portrayed in Vatican II is a pilgrim Church which does not have all the answers but is constantly striving to grow in wisdom and age and grace. Thus the conciliar documents reflect a more historical view of the Church, and even employ a historically conscious methodology.

THEOLOGICAL CONSEQUENCES

A historical worldview and a more historically conscious methodology will have important consequences when applied to the field of moral theology, for the manuals of moral theology today definitely reflect the classicist approach. In fact, there is a crisis in moral theology today precisely because such theology seems out of touch with modern man's understanding of reality. Of course I do not claim that everything modern man says about reality is correct, but then not everything in the classicist worldview was correct.

Sin infects the reality we know, and the Christian thinker can never simply accept as is whatever happens to be in vogue. However, the God of creation and redemption has called us to carry on his mission in time and space. The Christian, that is, is always called upon to view all things in the light of the gospel message. Whatever insights we may gain into reality and the world of creation can help us in our life.

Change and Development. The first important consequence of this new worldview and methodology affects our attitude toward change and development. The classical worldview, as we have seen, had little room for change. Only accidental changes could occur in a reality that was already constituted and known in its essence. Naturally such a view rejected any form of evolutionary theory because it was most difficult to explain evolution in such a system. On the other hand, the new worldview emphasizes the need for change. Change and growth do not affect merely the accidental constitution and knowledge of reality.

Man thirsts for truth and is constantly trying to find it. He is never satisfied with the knowledge he has at any given moment. Modern man realizes how incomplete this is, and he is continually probing to find out more about reality. The growth and progress of modern society demonstrate that development is absolutely necessary. The classicist methodology, on the other hand, claims a comparatively absolute and complete knowledge. Change naturally becomes a threat to the person who thinks that he already possesses truth. Of course, modern man recognizes that not all change is good and salutary. There will be mistakes on the way. However, the greatest error would be not to try at all.

Let us take as an example the dogmatic truth about the nature of Christ. The early christological councils proposed the formula of one person and two natures in Christ, a formula that is not present in the Scriptures. At the time there was an agonizing decision to go beyond the language of the Scriptures. But why does change have to stop in the fifth century? Might there not be an even better understanding of the natures and person of Christ today? Modern man might have different—and better—insights into the reality of Christ. Who can say that the fifth century was the final point in the development of our understanding?

When the classical worldview does speak of development, it places much emphasis on the fact that the truth always remains the same but it is expressed in different ways at different times. The same essential truth wears different clothing in different settings. However, does not the truth itself change and develop? There is more involved than just a different way of starting the same essential reality. Even in such sacrosanct dogmatic teachings there is room for real change and development.

The historical worldview realizes the constant need for growth and development, and also accepts the fact that mistakes and errors will always accompany such growth. But the attitude existing toward theology on the part of many priests in this country epitomizes the older worldview. (Perhaps such a mentality on the part of priests has been an obstacle in the path of Church renewal.) As seminarians, they learned all the truths of the Christian faith. There was no need, in this view, to continue study after ordination. The priest already possessed a certain knowledge of all the truths of the Christian faith.

Such an attitude also characterized the way in which theology was taught. Very little outside reading was done. The student simply memorized the notes of the professor which contained this certain knowledge. But the new methodology will bring with it a greater appreciation of the need for change and development in all aspects of the life and teaching of the Church.

Theology and Induction. Theology must adopt a more inductive methodology. Note that I am not advocating a unilaterally inductive and *a posteriori* approach for theology. However, in the past theology has attached too much importance to a deductive and somewhat *a priori* methodology. (Of course, as we shall see, with a more inductive approach moral theology can never again claim the kind of certitude it once did. At best, in some areas of conduct the ethician will be able to say that something clearly appears to be such and such at the present time.)

The classical methodology was a closed system, whereas a more historically conscious methodology proposes an open and heuristic approach. It will always remain open to new data and experience. Nothing is ever completely solved and closed, for an inductive methodology is more tentative and probing.

An inductive approach recognizes the existence of mistakes and errors, and even incorporates the necessary mechanism to overcome them. The building and manufacture of the Edsel automobile illustrates the possibility of error in a more inductive approach. Obviously, elaborate and expensive tests were run beforehand to see if there was a market for a car in the class of the projected Edsel. The decision to market the car was made on the best possible evidence. However, experience proved that the Edsel was a failure. A few years later, after similar exhaustive testing, the same company produced the Mustang, which has been a great success.

Theology, of course, is not the same as the other sciences. Progress and growth are much more evident in the area of the empirical sciences. However, the historicity of the gospel message and the historicity of man and the world demand a more historical approach in theology and the integration of a more inductive methodology. Particularly in the rather detailed minutiae of medical ethics, Catholic theology must learn to abandon the desire for the kind of absolute certitude which has characterized such moral theory in the past. Medicine, like science, is a field where man is constantly interfering with the processes of nature and the natural patterns of individual powers. But here the sole immediate effect of an action considered in itself cannot be the only determining element of morality. The action must be weighed in its total impact upon the persons involved and on the total community.

A more inductive approach in theology, especially in moral theology, will have to depend more on the experience of Christian people and all men of good will. The morality of particular actions cannot be judged apart from human experience. History seems to show that the changes which have occurred in Catholic morality have come about through the experience of all the people of the community. The fact that older norms did not come to grips with reality was first noticed in the experience of people.

Changes have occurred in the areas of usury, religious liberty, the right to silence, the role of love as a motive for marital relations, and other areas.[45] Certainly the rigorism of the earlier theologians on the place of procreation in marriage and marital intercourse has been modified by the experience of Christian people—for example, they held that marriage relations without the express purpose of procreation was at least venially sinful. And when the older theory of Church and State did not fit in with the historical circumstances of our day, John Courtney Murray showed that the living experience of people in the United States was more than just a toleration of an imperfect reality. In each case, experience showed the inadequacy of the older theory.

The older casuistry of mental reservation never set well with the experience of Christian people. The dissatisfaction with such casuistry played an important part in the understanding of lying now accepted by most contemporary theologians. Of course, just as theological methodology can never become totally inductive (the theologian always begins with the revelation of God in Christ), so too experience can never become the only factor in the formation of the Christian ethic. However, experience has a very important role to play.

Since the experience of Christian people and all men of good will is a source of moral knowledge, an ethician cannot simply spell out in advance everything that must be done by the doctor. And generally speaking, in other complicated areas of human life, the theologian cannot say that this or that action must always be performed. In many matters of medicine the ethician can merely tell the doctor to exercise his own prudent moral judgment. The patient and the doctor together must decide the feasibility of performing an operation by weighing the advantages against the risks.

Perhaps in some other matters now spelled out in the hospital code, more room should be left for conscientious decision by the doctor. The problem seems to reside in a system or theory that attaches exclusive moral importance to the physical structure of an act. At the very least, theologians must listen when doctors of good will are speaking to them. In fact, theologians must ask doctors to reveal their moral experience. The doctor must at least be listened to with respect when he honestly says that he thinks a raped 15-year-old girl who is a patient in a mental hospital should be aborted.

The Empirical Approach. Since a more historical methodology emphasizes the individual and the particular and employs a more inductive approach to knowing reality, Catholic theology will have to work much closer with the empirical and social sciences. It is these sciences that help man to pursue his goal and guide his development. A classicist approach which emphasized universals and essences was content with an almost exclusively deductive approach.

The Catholic Church in America today still reflects the fact that an older worldview did not appreciate or understand the need for the empirical and social sciences. The Catholic Church is probably the only very large corporation in America—I am here using "church" in the sense of a sociological entity and its administration—which does not have a research and development arm. How long could other corporations stay in existence without devoting huge sums to research and development? Heretofore, the Catholic Church has not realized the importance of change and growth.

Perhaps the crisis the Church faces today stems from a clinging to older forms of life when newer forms are required. However, without research and experimentation, who can decide what are the new forms which are needed? The answers are not all spelled out in the nature of things.

Certitude. As we have already seen, a changed theological methodology must necessarily result in a different attitude towards certitude. The classicist methodology aimed at absolute certitude. It was much easier come by in the classical approach, for this method cut through and disregarded individual, particular differences to arrive at immutable, abstract essences. In a deductive approach the conclusion follows by a logical connection from the premise. Provided the logic is correct, the conclusion is just as certain as the premise. Since circumstances cannot change the essences or universals, one can assert that the conclusion is now and always will be absolutely certain. There is no room for any change. A deductive methodology can be much more certain than an inductive approach.

The penchant for absolute certitude characterized the philosophical system which supports the concept of natural law as still found in medical ethics. Science, in this view, was defined as certain knowledge of the thing in its causes. Science, therefore, was oposed to opinion and theory. However, modern science does not aim at such certitude. Science today sees no opposition between science and opinion; in fact, scientific opinion and scientific theory form an essential part of the scientific vocabulary.

Absolute certitude actually would be the great enemy of the progress and growth that characterize modern life. Once absolute certitude is reached, there is no sense in continuing research except to clear up a few peripheral matters.[46] In the Thomistic framework there was really no room for progress in scientific fields. And there was little or no room for development within the sciences, so conceived, because the first principles of the science itself were already known. The revolutionary approaches within the modern sciences show the fallacy in the Thomistic understanding of science.[47]

A more historically conscious methodology does not pretend to have or even to aim at absolute certitude. Since time, history, and individual differences are important, they cannot be dismissed as mere accidents which do not affect essential truth. This approach does not emphasize abstract essences, but concrete phenomena. Conclusions are based on the observations and experience gleaned in a more inductive approach. Such an approach can never strive for absolute certitude.

Modern science views reality in this more historical manner and consequently employs this more inductive approach. The progress of scientific and technical mankind demands a continuing search for an ever better way. Even the Volkswagen is constantly being improved, and may be quite different in ten years. An inductive methodology can never cease its working. It constantly runs new experiments and observations, for modern science aims at the best for the present time, but realizes that new progress must be made for the future.

The Magisterium. A historically conscious methodology also entails important consequences for a proper understanding of the role of the hierarchical magisterium. Catholic medical moralists often speak in terms of eternal and immutable moral norms. But awareness of the historical condition of man means that older statements of the magisterium may no longer be adequate today.

Scripture scholars have freed the Church from a literal fundamentalism through a demonstration of the historical influence present in the formation of the Scriptures. Unfortunately, the statements of the magisterium are still accepted in a somewhat fundamentalist manner by many Catholics. These statements must also be seen in the light of the historical, cultural, and scientific circumstances of the times in which they were composed.

Murray's claim, for example, that the newer teaching on Church and State reflects the different historical reality of the twentieth century should serve as a salutary reminder to those who feel it is enough merely to cite magisterial documents from a former time. Obviously, the theory of Church and State proposed by Murray did not become true only at the moment when *Pacem in Terris* or the Declaration on Religious Liberty was promulgated in Rome.

Even more importantly, magisterial teaching generally reflects an older theological methodology and a one-sided hierarchical view of the Church, both of which today have changed. In the past the magisterial moral teachings were stated in the form of norms that were thought to be absolutely and immutably true. However, a more inductive approach will not always claim that type of certitude.

The emphasis on human experience and the Church as the people of God will also tend to leave matters more open ended. There are many ways in which the Church does teach, and should teach, other than by pronouncements of the hierarchical magisterium. In fact, if the magisterium is going to be relevant in the modern world, then the claim to absolute certitude becomes a hindrance. To be meaningful, the magisterium has to raise its voice or try to clarify issues long before such certitude is at all possible. If one waits for absolute certitude before speaking, one can be assured that his utterance will be either meaningless or irrelevant when the pronouncement is finally made.

The whole teaching Church must be willing to assume the risk of being wrong and making mistakes. In the modern world guidance for Christians will not be given in terms of absolute statements, but in terms of what appears to be the most Christian way of acting at a given time. A more historical understanding of reality and a more historically conscious methodology definitely alter our understanding of past statements of the magisterium (not that they are necessarily wrong today) and also significantly affect the way in which the Church must teach in the future.

Positive Law. Likewise, the modern view of positive law attributes a much changed and reduced role to it. Canon law exists primarily to preserve order and harmony in the society of the people of God, and not to serve as a guide for the life of the individual Christian.[48] Nor are civil laws primarily a guide for man's moral conduct. Civil law as such is not primarily interested in the true, the good, and the beautiful. Civil law has the very limited aim of preserving the public order.[49]

Society functions better not when law dictates to everyone what is to be done, but rather when law tries to create the climate in which individuals and smaller groups within the society can exercise their creativity and development for the good of the total community.[50] No longer is society under a master plan minutely controlled by the rules of the society. Rather, modern society's progress and growth come from the initiative of people within the society. Thus, the more historically minded worldview has a different perspective on the meaning and role of law in human life. Natural and human law are no longer seen as a detailed plan which guides and directs all human activity.

The Nature of Reality. A classicist worldview tends to see reality in terms of substances and natures which exist in themselves apart from any relations with other substances and natures. Every substance has its own nature or principle of operation. Within every acorn, for example, there is a nature which directs the acorn into becoming an oak tree. The acorn will not become a maple tree or an elm tree because it has the nature of an oak tree. The growth and "activity" of the thing is determined by the nature inscribed in it. Growth is the intrinsic unfolding of the nature within the substance.

Notice how such a view of reality affects morality. Human action depends upon human nature. Human action is its intrinsic unfolding in man. Nature, therefore, tells what actions are to be done and what actions are to be avoided. To determine the morality of an action, one must study its nature. The above description, although a caricature of Thomas' teaching, does represent the approach to morality of the kind of unilaterally substantialist view of reality generally assumed in the manuals.

The contemporary view sees reality more in terms of relations than of substances and natures. Man is not thought of as a being totally constituted in himself, whose life is the unfolding of the nature he already possesses. There seemingly can be no real human growth and history when future development is already determined by what is present here and now. This is the point of difference between a naturalist view and a historicist view.[51]

According to the modern, more relational view, reality does not consist of separate substances existing completely independent of each other. Reality can be understood only in terms of the relations that exist among the individual beings. A particular being can never be adequately considered in itself, apart from its relations with other beings and the fullness of being. An emphasis on relations rather than substances surely cannot be foreign to Catholic thinking, since theologians have spoken of the persons of the Trinity as relations.

Human experience also reminds us of the importance of relationship even in constituting ourselves as human persons. A relational understanding of reality will never see morality solely in terms of the individual substance or nature. Morality depends primarily not on the substance viewed in itself but on the individual seen in relationship to other beings. Unfortunately, medical ethics frequently derives its conclusions from the nature of a faculty or the physical causality of an action seen only in itself and not in relationship with the total person and the entire community.

Aristotle. A brief defense of Aristotle is necessary here to avoid false impressions. Aristotle did not have a static view of reality. Nature itself was a principle of operation that tended toward a goal, but the goal was specific rather than individual. The emphasis was on the species of oak tree, that is, and not on the individual oak as such. But Aristotle did not conceive of man as he did of lesser life.

As an acute observer of the human scene, he realized that most men do not achieve their goal of happiness and self-fulfillment. Man, he thought, does not possess an intrinsic dynamism which necessarily achieves its goal. Man's happiness, consequently, depends not on an intrinsic tending to perfection according to the demands of his nature, but rather his happiness depends on extrinsic circumstances.

Man has no intrinsic orientation (a nature) necessarily bringing about his perfection; rather, according to Aristotle, he depends more on the contingent and the accidental. Man needs freedom, health, wealth, friends, and luck to find his fulfillment.[52] Notice that Aristotle himself constructed a theory of man that answers many of the strictures made against textbook natural law theories today.

But the classicist worldview of the manuals tends to see the world in a very detailed pattern. The function of man is to correspond to this structure (the "natural law") as minutely outlined. Man puts together the different pieces of human behavior much like putting together the pieces of a jigsaw puzzle. He finds the objective pieces already existing and just fits them together. The more historically minded worldview, on the other hand, sees man as creating and shaping the plan of the world. Man does not merely respect the intrinsic nature and finalities of the individual pieces of the pattern. Rather, man interferes to form new pieces and new patterns.

A Transcendental Methodology. A different worldview, as we have seen, affects our understanding of reality. The older stressed the objectivity of reality. In this view truth consists in the mind's grasp of the reality itself. A clear distinction exists between the object and the subject. Meaning exists in the objective reality, and the subject perceives the meaning already present in reality. A historically conscious methodology must avoid the pitfall of a total relativism which occasionally creeps into Christianity in various forms of cultural Christianity. Man needs to understand the ontological foundations of historical development; the Christian needs to understand all things in the light of the uniqueness of the once-for-all event of Christ Jesus. Both contemporary Protestant (for example, Macquarrie, Ogden) and Catholic (Rahner, Lonergan) scholars are addressing themselves to this problem.

Modern thought and culture stress more the creative aspects (both intellectual and affective) of the subject. Modern art reveals the feelings and emotions of the subject rather than portraying an objective picture of reality. The modern cinema confronts the viewer with a very subjective view of reality that calls for imagination and perceptivity on the part of the viewer. Catholic theologians are now speaking in somewhat similar terms of a transcendental methodology in theology.

Karl Rahner has observed that natural law should be approached in this way.[53] A transcendental methodology talks about the conditions and structure in the subject necessary for it to come to know reality, for this very structure is part of the knowing process. Bernard Lonergan speaks about meaning in much the same way.[54] Man's meaning can change such basic realities as community, family, state, etc. Meaning involves more than just the apprehension of the objective reality as something "out there."

A note of caution is necessary. Although Lonergan, for example, espouses a more historical consciousness and a transcendental method, at the same time he strongly proclaims a critical realism in epistemology. Lonergan definitely holds for propositions and objective truth, and truth as a correspondence. However, for Lonergan human knowing is a dynamic structure; intentionality and meaning pertain to that objectivity. He reacts against a "naive realism" or a "picture book" type of objectivity.

The problem in the past was that the objectivity of knowledge was identified with the analogy of the objectivity of the sense of sight. "Objective" is that which I see out there. Such a concept of objectivity is false because it identifies objectivity with just one of the properties of one of the operations involved in human knowing. Lonergan rejects both a naive realism and idealism.[55] It seems, however, that the objectivity talked about in medical moral textbooks is often a naive, picture-book objectivity.

The concept of natural law presupposed in Catholic medical ethics definitely reflects a classicist worldview, which sees a very precise and well-defined pattern existing for the world and man's moral behavior. This ordering and pattern is called the natural law. Natural law reigns in the area of the necessary.

Within the area marked out by the pattern showing the absolute and the necessary is the contingent and the changing. Just as natural law governs the life of man in the area of the principles common to all men, so positive law, both civil and ecclesiastical, governs the life of man in the contingent and the changing circumstances of life. The plan for the world is thus worked out in great detail in the mind of the creator, and man's whole purpose is to conform himself to the divine plan as made known in the natural and positive laws. (Despite the classical worldview of his day, in his system Thomas did leave room for the virtue of prudence and the creativity of the individual. However, the place later assigned to prudence in textbooks was drastically reduced, and thus Thomas' teaching was distorted.)

But a more historically minded worldview does not look upon reality as a plan whose features are sketched in quite particular detail according to an unchanging pattern. Modern man's moral existence does not primarily call for conformity to such a detailed and unchanging plan. He looks upon existence as a vocation to find the meaning of human existence creatively in his own life and experience. The meaning of human life is not already given in some pre-existing pattern or plan.

Perhaps the characterization I have given of the two worldviews tends to be oversimplified. For one thing, the points of difference between them have been delineated without any attempt to show the similarities. The differences in many areas of morality—for example, the understanding and living of the evangelical norm of love and forgiveness—would be minimal. The reasoning developed in this section has prescinded, as well, from the question of growth and development in human values and morals. However, in the modern world of science and technology, characterized by instant communication, rapid transportation, and changing sociological patterns, it is clear that man needs a more historical worldview and a more historically conscious methodology than the person who lived in a comparatively static and closed society.

SOME RE-EVALUATIONS

The contemporary dialogue of Catholic ethicians with other men of good will, together with the demands of renewal, have helped Catholic ethicians in trying to re-evaluate natural law and its place in Catholic theological thought. The next few paragraphs will try to summarize briefly some of the recent investigations about natural law.

Textbooks frequently leave the impression that the natural law is a very detailed plan for human existence, inscribed in man's nature. A better understanding of man's mastery over brute nature and the acceptance of a historical worldview should do much to refute the idea of a natural law as such a plan. However, the impression still remains among Catholics that the natural law is a monolithic, ethical system with an agreed upon body of moral content.

A Changing Concept. The assertion is not true. Historical investigation shows that numerous thinkers have used the term, but the term had different meanings for many of them.[56] Aristotle spoke of nature as the principle of operation in things, but man does not necessarily have a nature which brings him to his goal.[57] The Stoics used the term "nature" in reference to the whole cosmos and the intelligibility of the order enshrined in the universe. Gerard Watson has concluded that the term "natural law" for the Stoics had a meaning about as general as our term "morality."[58]

The fact that all those who employed the term "natural law" did not mean the same thing by the term is also evident from the divergency of opinions on the morality of certain human actions. A knowledge of history should destroy the myth of a monolithic, philosophical system of natural law in existence from Greek philosophy down to the present day. The Scriptures, for example, do not use the word "nature" in a technical way. In St. Paul's famous passage in Romans 2:13-15, he does not claim that man without Christ or grace can keep the works of the law.[59] The Fathers of the Church understood nature in a historical sense; thus following them, Gratian, who codified canon law, described the natural law as that which is contained in the law and the Gospels.[60] We have already looked at Ulpian's conception of it.

The nominalistic scholastics who came after Thomas did not mean by nature the same thing he did. Those who spoke of the natural rights of man in the seventeenth and eighteenth centuries did not accept Thomistic philosophy. Nature was understood in many different ways: some opposed nature to spirit; others opposed nature to the positive laws and conventions of society that were destroying the true dignity of man; economists used nature as opposed to a controlled or regulated economy. All of these people could use the term "natural law," but they all meant something different.

Natural Law and Catholicism. The fact that natural law is not a determined philosophical system, with an accepted code of ethical conduct in existence from the earliest times of human history, has repercussions on the place of natural law in the development of Catholic moral teaching. Catholic textbooks give the impression that the moral teaching on a particular point came into existence through the application of the system of natural law to a particular moral problem. However, if there was not coherent philosophical system of the natural law (at least before St. Thomas), then natural law cannot be the real reason explaining why the Church judged such conduct to be wrong.

Take as an example the traditional teaching on birth control. Clement of Alexandria did not solve the moral problem by calling together a study group of natural law theoreticians.[61] The teaching on birth control, like the teaching on the vast majority of other moral matters in the Church, came into existence independently of the natural law theory. Most of our moral teaching was already formed long before Thomas ever lived.

The natural law, for the most part, has been used in recent centuries as a systematic explanation of a moral teaching that already existed independently of the theory of natural law. But in the earlier Church, the experience of Christian people seems to have been a most important criterion. Reasons were then given to bolster the already existing teachings.

Theologians traditionally have taught that masturbation was wrong and even gravely so, but the theologians could not agree on the reasons for such a condemnation.[62] Even many proponents of the condemnation of artificial contraception admit that the natural law reasons adduced are not convincing. The reasons proposed by Thomas for the malice of fornication can be obviated by the use of contraceptives.[63] It is clear that the vast majority of Catholic moral teaching did not come into existence by an application of natural law theory to a particular question. In fact, the sovereign freedom of the word of God means that theology can never be tied to any one philosophical understanding of reality, although there are some philosophical theories that are incompatible with the Christian understanding of faith. Catholic theologians do not have to defend natural law apologetically, as if Catholic moral teaching totally depends on such a theory.[64]

Absolute Norms. The characteristic of natural law that has been most attacked is the tendency to establish absolute norms of moral behavior. However, scholars are realizing that Thomas himself did not maintain, at least in theory, the existence of moral norms that never admit of exceptions.[65]

Thomas admits that once reason leaves the first principles of the natural law (do good; act according to reason), there is a possibility of exceptions to the general norm. Speculative truths do not admit of exceptions when applied to particular cases. But matter itself is changeable and, as it were, matter can get in the way of the principle and block its application because of particular circumstances.[66]

Likewise, Thomas admitted the exceptions to the absolute norms mentioned in the Old Testament: Abraham's willingness to kill Isaac, the polygamy of the patriarchs, the stealing by the Israelites, the fornication of Hosea. Thomas occasionally explains these exceptions by saying that God can intervene in the moral order by a miracle just as he can intervene in the physical order by a miracle.[67] (Interestingly, one Protestant theologian recently gave a talk on situation ethics entitled, "Law and Miracle."[68])

Thomas himself, in principle, admits the possibility of exceptions to the particular norms of morality that are derived from the first principles of the moral life. In addition to a more historical consciousness and the intervention of man in the physical laws of nature, other factors such as a knowledge of cultural relativities and anthropological data have forced theologians to reconsider the absolute demands that have been made in the past in the name of natural law.[69] One Thomistic scholar concludes that the primary principles of the natural law are merely formal and tautological, while the derivative principles are disputable and not accepted by all.[70] Thus, at least in theory, Catholic scholars admit that the natural law is not as absolute as many had thought in the past.

Two Ambiguities. There appears to be an ambiguity connected with the term "natural law." Our very brief recapitulation of its historical development shows the many different senses in which the word "natural" has been used.[71] The term is ambiguous at best, and frequently leaves the impression (if not the reality itself) of being identified with the physical laws of nature.

The term "law" also seems to be ambiguous and misleading. Contemporary Catholic philosophers and theologians point out that the Thomist notion of law has been misinterpreted by those who often call themselves Thomists.[72] Nominalistic influence has altered this notion. In general, nominalistic tendencies accentuate the role of the will: something is right because it is commanded. The Thomist notion is more realistic: something is commanded because it is good.

Some have suggested apparent deficiencies in the Thomistic understanding of law because the will of the legislator is not mentioned. However, Thomas places the obliging force of law not in the will of the legislator but in the reality itself—the ordering of reason. If he is rightly understood, he cannot be accused of legalism. Law for Thomas does not have the connotations of external obligation and legal sanctions. He makes the will of the legislator conform to the reality itself.

Law for him means an ordering of reason. Natural law is the divine plan, the divine ordering, insofar as it exists in the rational creature. If the Thomistic understanding of law were accepted, some of the ambiguities connected with the term "law" would cease. But even if his concept of law were properly understood, difficulties arise from the classical worldview inherent in such an approach.

The connotations of the word "law" definitely recall absolute norms and sanctions. The Thomistic notion presupposes that man's primary function is to conform to a plan which is already existing. Also a classical worldview at least insinuates that the plan is quite detailed and exact. However, contemporary thought accentuates man's call to become creatively a more human person within the community of mankind.

The fact that theologians are today calling into question the absoluteness of the "natural law" also argues against the retention of such a term. One receives the impression that in the past Catholic thinkers have strained to call something "natural law" just so they could justify its absolute prohibition. Nature says this; therefore, man can never change it. Both in the popular mind and also in the argumentation of theologians the term "natural law" has led to an unwarranted emphasis on the absolute character of the norms sanctioned by it.[73] The very term "natural law" thus seems inaccurate and misleading.

There does, however, seem to be a real validity for theological ethics behind the traditional theory of natural law. The basic truth is that a source of ethical wisdom and knowledge apart from the explicit revelation of God in Scripture exists. A morality based on the reality of man and his history in the world definitely is a valid source of ethical knowledge. A frequent complaint against natural law theory has been the insistence on absolute norms. However, such an insistence is not necessarily of the essence of a morality based on man and human community in the world. In the area of social morality, for example, Catholic natural law theory has spoken a relevant message.[74]

A Christian Convergence. A convergence seems to be growing in Christian ethics. More and more, Catholic theologians are coming to realize the overemphasis on absolute norms in natural law theory. In addition, a more historical worldview should overcome some Protestant fears about the Catholic understanding of natural law. The contemporary understanding of nature and grace in Catholic theology should also allay some Protestant fears about the "natural" in Catholic theology. And Catholic moral theologians are more and more realizing the presence and influence of sin in the ethical problems facing the Christian. However, many Protestant ethicians see the need for a source of ethical knowledge apart from the explicit revelation of God in the Scriptures.

Protestant ethicians have used different approaches to the problem. Emil Brunner speaks of the orders of creation.[75] Bonhoeffer shows the divine mandates at work in history.[76] Reinhold Niebuhr stresses the importance of justice.[77] John C. Bennett writes about the natural law, and lately he refers to common ground morality.[78] Paul Ramsey accepts a description of his ethical theory in terms of love transforming natural justice.[79] James Gustafson has maintained that Christian social ethics must have a number of different starting points, including Christian revelation and faith, an analysis of self, and an understanding of social structures and processes.[80]

There are many reasons underlying the realization of the need for a source of ethical wisdom apart from the explicit revelation in Christ. Perhaps the most contemporary reason in Protestant thought is the emphasis on a theology of secularity and a reaction against transcendence. The meaning of history and the importance of life in this world are the main theological issues of the day. Other reasons include: the need to cooperate in social questions of poverty, race, and peace with all men of good will; the insufficiencies of the Scriptures, especially in dealing with the complex ethical problems of urban life; and the realization that two-thirds of the world does not know Christ.

I believe that in the future the ethical convergence of Protestant and Catholic thought will be even more evident. Historical differences fade away as Christians seriously examine together the problems confronting the world today. I do not say that the future will find a perfect harmony among all Christian ethicians, but the differences will not be based on something that is peculiar to Roman Catholic thinking.

Catholic ethicians themselves will probably be divided on a number of issues, even on those issues which up to the present have seemingly been accepted by Catholic moral theologians. Catholic theoreticians realize the ambiguities and problems connected with the textbook approach to natural law.[81] Newer theories are being proposed in terms of an ethic based on person or community. These newer theories obviate some of the traditional objections to natural law theory and at the same time call for a different approach to moral problems, especially in the area of medical morality.

Recent Catholic Reconstructions. Robert O. Johann, has been proposing his understanding of natural law in various publications in recent years. Johann sees his theory in continuity with traditional natural law because morality has an ontological foundation. Johann objects to the older understanding of natural law because of its absolute character, and also because of its substantive view of reality.

Things cannot be considered only in themselves, exclu

sively in terms of the principle of operation which is present in each thing. Rather, reality exists in relationship with other beings, and ultimately with Being itself. There is something outside the situation which prevents morality from degenerating into sentimentality. All moral requirements are grounded in Being itself, so that moral values remain objective. Everything else is relativized by its relationship to Being. The general moral norm is the promotion of Being.[82]

Note the implications of such a theory in the area of medical morals. Johann's system logically leads to many of the conclusions about particular medical moral problems which were mentioned in the beginning of this chapter. The moral understanding of the relativizing of all individual things and actions in the light of Being leads to a denial of absolute norms based on the structure of an individual act viewed in itself apart from its relations with other beings and the fullness of being.

W. van der Marck, O.P., also rejects the textbook consideration of human acts and the natural law. An act cannot be judged merely according to its physical structure. Traditional theology has neglected the intersubjectivity of human actions. For him the ultimate norm of morality is not the nature of an individual thing or man or the physical structure of an action, but rather the community-forming or community-breaking aspect of a particular action, its relationship to the community. The human act is primarily a means of communication and a way of building up the community. Only in such a light, and not by a consideration of abstract natures or physical structures, can an action be judged.[83]

Bishop Simons of India also realizes the need to abandon a moral theory based on the inner purpose or construction of a particular organ or action considered in itself. The ultimate criterion of morality, he suggests, is what the good or welfare of man—individually or socially—demands. The moral judgment depends on all mankind and springs from truly human values. Simons calls for the need to weigh the results of the actions, but the individual act and its consequences are subordinated to the consequences that would follow if the action were permitted as a general rule.[84]

John G. Milhaven, S.J., has also questioned the principle that the essential purpose of a particular action suffices to determine its morality. Milhaven wants to see things in the light of the general purpose of God and creation; consequently, more empirical evidence would be necessary to set up an absolute moral norm.[85]

In general, the newer proposals reject the idea of a morality determined by an investigation of a particular being or a particular faculty viewed in its essential nature apart from the relationship to the person and the wider relationship to the community or even Being itself. The newer approaches have a continuity with the older understanding of natural law, but they look upon reality in a different way. Basically, the newer theories are reactions to the difficulties with traditional natural law theory mentioned earlier in this chapter.

The newer theories definitely will have an effect on the textbook understanding of natural law as applied to medical morality. Such theories would not be prone to admit, for example, that direct killing, or direct abortion, or direct sterilization, based on the sole immediate effect of the action, could become an absolute prohibition. Likewise, the newer theories do not seem compatible with the absolute prohibition of the voluntary emission of male semen, or the absolute necessity of conception taking place as the result of the act of sexual intercourse.

The call for a change in the current Catholic understanding of medical morality has already begun. This study has tried to show some of the individual points of dissatisfaction with the present teaching and also to put in a historical context some of the reasons underlying them. The newer approaches to natural law theory (if the name is to be continued) all logically come to the same conclusion: the need to change the theory underlying Catholic medical morality and to work out the concrete applications of that theory.

NOTES

1. E.g., Joseph Fletcher, *Situation Ethics: The New Morality* (Philadelphia: Westminster Press, 1966), p. 21; Edward LeRoy Long, Jr., *A Survey of Christian Ethics* (New York: Oxford University Press, 1967), pp. 167-185.

2. General discussions of medical ethics by American Catholic authors in the last two decades include: B. J. Ficarra, *Newer Medical Problems in Ethics and Surgery* (Westminster, Md.: Newman Press, 1949); Frederick L. Good and Otis F. Kelly, *Marriage, Morals, and Medical Ethics* (New York: P. J. Kenedy, 1951); Edwin F. Healy, S.J., *Medical Ethics* (Chicago: Loyola University Press, 1956); Gerald Kelly, S.J., *Medico-Moral Problems* (St. Louis: The Catholic Hospital Association, 1958); John P. Kenny, O.P., *Principles of Medical Ethics,* 2nd ed. (Westminster, Md.: Newman Press, 1961); Charles J. McFadden, O.S.A., *Medical Ethics,* 4th ed. (Philadelphia: F. A. Davis, 1958); Timothy O'Connell, *Morality in Medicine* (Paterson: St. Anthony Press, 1953); Thomas G. O'Donnell, S.J., *Morals in Medicine*, 2nd ed. (Westminster, Md.: Newman Press, 1959). Also there are a number of Catholic journals devoted to morality and medicine: England: *Catholic Medical Quarterly;* France: *Cahiers Laënnec* (five volumes of articles from *Cahiers Laënnec* have been published in the United States by Newman Press under the title *New Problems in Medical Ethics*, ed. Dom Peter Flood, O.S.B.); Belgium: *Saint-Luc Médical;* U.S.A.: *Linacre Quarterly*.

3. The textbooks mentioned in note 2 give the pertinent references to papal teachings and other magisterial pronouncements.

4. *National Catholic Reporter,* April, 19, 1967.

5. John Marshall, *Catholics, Marriage, and Contraception* (Baltimore: Helicon, 1965), pp. 96-98; Richard A. McCormick, S.J., "Practical and Theoretical Considerations," in *The Problem of Population,* Vol. III (Notre Dame: University of Notre Dame Press, 1965), pp. 61-67. The minority report of the Papal Commission admitted that the natural law arguments against artificial contraception are not entirely convincing; thus, "men need the help of the teaching of the Church, explained and applied under the leadership of the magisterium, so that they can with certitude and security embrace the way, the truth, and the life."

6. Healy, p. 171. In his allocation to the Italian Catholic Union of Midwives (*AAS*, 43 (1951), 835-854), Pius XII stated: "Direct sterilization, that which aims at making procreation impossible both as means and end, is a grave violation of the moral law, and therefore illicit" (N.C.W.C. translation). Cf. "Casti

Connubii," *AAS*, 22 (1930), 564, 565; and also the decree of the Holy Office of February 22, 1940, *AAS*, 32 (1940), 73.

7. John C. Ford, S.J., and Gerald Kelly, S.J., *Contemporary Moral Theology: Marriage Questions* (Westminster, Md.: Newman Press, 1963), pp. 315-337.

8. Pope Pius XII, Address to the Hematologists, *AAS*, 50 (1958), 734 ff.

9. For a complete bibliography, see Ambrogio Valsecchi, "La discussione morale sui progestativi," *La Scuola Cattolica*, 93 (1965), supplemento 2, 157*-216*. A word of caution is in order. Many of the authors mentioned in Valsecchi's article have since changed their opinions about the morality of contraception. Likewise, some of the authors cited in the present study have changed the opinions recorded here.

10. The Ethical Directives of the Catholic Hospital Association are included as appendices by Healy, McFadden and O'Donnell.

11. Pope Pius XII, Address to the Second World Congress of Fertility and Sterility, May 19, 1956, *AAS*, 48 (1956), 472; Address to Italian Urologists, October 8, 1953, *AAS*, 45 (1953), 678; Decree of the Holy Office, August 2, 1929, *AAS*, 21 (1929), 490.

12. Bernard Häring, C.SS.R., proposed such an opinion as probable at a course for professors and others interested in moral theology at Regis College, Toronto, Canada, July, 1963. See L. M. Weber, "Onanismus," *Lexicon für Theologie und Kirche* (Freiburg: Herder, 1962), Vol. 7, 1157-1158.

13. Pope Pius XII, Address to the Fourth World Congress of Catholic Doctors, Rome, September 29, 1949, *AAS*, 41 (1949), 560; also in later addresses, *AAS*, 43 (1951), 850; *AAS*, 48 (1956), 469-471.

14. Kelly, p. 242.

15. P. Knauer, S.J., "La détermination du bien et du mal morale par le principe du double effet," *Nouvelle Revue Théologique*, 87 (1965), 356-376; W. van der Marck, O.P., *Love and Fertility* (London: Sheed and Ward, 1965), pp. 35-63.

16. T. Lincoln Bouscaren, S.J., *Ethics of Ectopic Operations*, 2nd ed. (Milwaukee: Bruce Publishing Co., 1944); Kelly, pp. 105-110.

17. van der Marck, p. 59, 60.

18. Bert J. Cunningham, C.M., *The Morality of Organic Transplantation* (Washington: The Catholic University of America Press, 1944); O'Donnell, pp. 122-131. For a fine summary of the controversy and pertinent bibliography, see Kelly, pp. 245-252.

19. Archbishop Denis E. Hurley, "A New Moral Principle," *The Furrow,* 17 (1966), 621.

20. The specific question of the double effect and its relation to abortion are considered extensively also in the chapter by Cornelius van der Poel. They are mentioned here as illustrations of the dissatisfaction in certain areas of medical morality.

21. Jean Marie Aubert, "Le Droit Naturel: ses avatars historiques et son avenir," *Supplément de la Vie Spirituelle,* 81 (1967), especially 298 ff.

22. *The Digest* or *Pandects of Justinian,* Book 1, t. 1, n. 1-4.

23. Odon Lottin, *Le Droit Naturel chez Saint Thomas d'Aquin et ses prédécesseurs,* 2nd ed. (Bruges: Charles Beyaert, 1931), p. 62.

24. *In IV Sent.* d. 33, q.1, a.1, ad 4.

25. *In V Ethic.,* lect. 12.

26. *I-II,* q.90, a.1, ob.3; q.96, a.5, ob.3; q.97, a.2; *II-II,* q.57, a.3, ob.1 and *in corp.*

27. *I-II,* q.95, a.4

28. *II-II,* q.57, a.3

29. E.g., H. Noldin et al., *Summa Theologiae Moralis: De Castitate,* 36th ed. (Oeniponte: F. Rauch, 1958), pp. 21-43.

30. Decree of the Holy Office on the ends of marriage, April 1, 1944, *AAS,* 36 (1944), 103. Also various addresses of Pius XII: *AAS,* 33 (1941), 422; 43 (1951), 835-854.

31. Regis Araud, S.J., "Évolution de la Théologie du Mariage," *Cahiers Laënnec,* 27 (1967), 56-71; W. van der Marck, O.P., "De recente ontwikkelingen in de theologie van het huwelijk," *Tijdschrift voor Theologie,* 7 (1967), 127-140. English summary on page 140.

32. Gerard Watson, "The Early History of Natural Law," *The Irish Theological Quarterly,* 33 (1966), 65-74.

33. John L. Russell, S.J., "The Concept of Natural Law," *The Heythrop Journal,* 6 (1965), 434-438; Pierre Colin, "Ambiguïtés du mot nature," *Supplément de la Vie Spirituelle,* 81 (1967), 253-255.

34. Charles E. Curran, "Masturbation and Objectively Grave Matter: An Exploratory Discussion," *Proceedings of the Catholic Theological Society of America,* 21 (1966), 95-109.

35. H. Noldin et al., *Summa Theologiae Moralis,* Vol. II: *De Praeceptis* (Oeniponte: F. Rauch, 1959), pp. 553-560; E. F. Regatillo, S.J., and M. Zalba, S.J., *Theologiae Moralis Summa,* Vol. II (Matriti: Biblioteca de Autores Cristianos, 1953), 1000-1018.

36. J. A. Dorszynski, *Catholic Teaching about the Morality of Falsehood* (Washington: Catholic University of America Press, 1949); Francis J. Connell, C.SS.R., *More Answers to Today's*

Moral Problems, ed. Eugene J. Weitzel, C.S.V. (Washington: Catholic University of America Press, 1965), p. 123, 124. Augustine had at one time accepted the distinction between falsehood and lying, but he later changed his opinion.

37. Bernard Lonergan, S.J., *Collection* (New York: Herder and Herder, 1967), pp. 252-267; Lonergan, "A Transition from a Classicist Worldview to Historical Mindedness," in *Law for Liberty: The Role of Law in the Church Today*, ed. James E. Biecher (Baltimore: Helicon Press, 1967). Lonergan along with other theologians such as Maréchal, Rahner, and Metz maintains that although Thomas Aquinas reflected a classical worldview, the followers of Thomas distorted his teaching especially in such areas as the emphasis on a deductive methodology and a non-relational understanding of being.

38. John Courtney Murray, S.J., "The Declaration on Religious Freedom," *Concilium: Moral Theology*, Vol. 5, n. 2 (May 1966), 3-10.

39. Eulalio R. Baltazar, *Teilhard and the Supernatural* (Baltimore: Helicon Press, 1966); Leslie Dewart, *The Future of Belief* (New York: Herder and Herder, 1966). Lonergan espouses historical mindedness but strenuously opposes the approach of Dewart. See Lonergan, "The Dehellenization of Dogma," *Theological Studies*, 28 (1967), 336-351.

40. Murray, *Concilium*, 7-10.

41. John Courtney Murray, S.J., *The Problem of Religious Freedom* (Westminster, Md.: Newman, 1965).

42. John Courtney Murray, S.J., "Freedom, Authority, Community," *America* (December 3, 1966), 735.

43. *Gaudium et Spes* (The Pastoral Constitution on the Church in the Modern World), n. 44. For a competent one-volume translation of the documents of Vatican II, see *The Documents of Vatican II*,ed. Walter M. Abbott, S.J. (New York: America Press and Association Press, 1966.

44. Karl Rahner, S.J., *The Dynamic Element in the Church* (New York: Herder and Herder, 1964).

45. Daniel Maguire, *Moral Absolutes and the Magisterium*, (Washington: Corpus Papers, 1970).

46. Herbert Butterfield, *The Origins of Modern Science, 1300-1800* (New York: Macmillan, 1951); Lonergan, *Collection*, p. 259 ff.

47. Andreas van Melsen, "Natural Law and Evolution," *Concilium: Church and World*, Vol. 6, n. 3 (June, 1967), 24-29.

48. *Law for Liberty: The Role of Law in the Church Today*, *passim*.

49. *Documents of Vatican II*, p. 686, n. 20. The footnote on

the role of civil law was written by John Courtney Murray.

50. Thomas B. McDonough, "Distribution of Contraceptives by the Welfare Department: A Catholic Response," in *The Problem of Population,* Vol. II (Notre Dame: University of Notre Dame Press, 1964), pp. 94-118.

51. Douglas Sturm, "Naturalism, Historicism, and Christian Ethics: Toward a Christian Doctrine of Natural Law," *The Journal of Religion,* 44 (1964), 40-51. Note again that some Catholic thinkers see in the excessive emphasis on *res in se* apart from any relational consideration a distortion of the understanding of St. Thomas.

52. Russell, *The Heythrop Journal,* 6 (1965), 434-438.

53. Karl Rahner, S.J., "Theology and Anthropology," in *The Word in History,* ed. T. Patrick Burke (New York: Sheed and Ward, 1966), pp. 1-23; Rahner, "Naturrecht," *Lexikon für Theologie und Kirche,* Vol. 7, 827-828.

54. Lonergan, "Dimensions of Meaning," *Collection,* pp. 252-267.

55. Lonergan, *Collection,* pp. 221-239; *Theological Studies,* 28 (1967), 337-351.

56. Philippe Delhaye, *Permanence du Droit Naturel* (Louvain: Editions Nauwelaerts, 1960); Heinrich A. Rommen, *The Natural Law* (St. Louis: B. Herder, 1947); Yves R. Simon, *The Tradition of Natural Law* (New York: Fordham University Press, 1965); Lottin, *Le Droit Naturel chez Saint Thomas d'Aquin et ses Prédécesseurs;* Pierre Colin, *Supplément de la Vie Spirituelle,* 81 (1967), 251-268; Jean Marie Aubert, *Supplément de la Vie Spirituelle,* 81 (1967), 282-324.

57. Russell, *The Heythrop Journal,* 6 (1965), 434-446.

58. Watson, *The Irish Theological Quarterly,* 33 (1966), 65-74.

59. For a summary of the different exegetical opinions, see Stanislaus Lyonnet, S.J., "Lex naturalis et justificatio Gentilium," *Verbum Domini,* 41 (1963), 238-242.

60. Delhaye, 44-53; *Decretum Gratiani,* p.I, d.1.

61. John T. Noonan, Jr., *Contraception: A History of its Treatment by the Catholic Theologians and Canonists* (Cambridge: Harvard University Press, 1965), pp. 56-107.

62. V. Vangheluwe, "De Intrinseca et Gravi Malitia Pollutionis," *Collationes Brugenses,* 48 (1952), 108-115.

63. *II-II,* q.154, a.2.

64. The relationship between natural law theory and the magisterial teaching of the Catholic Church as well as a detailed explanation of the "non-absolute" character of natural law may be found in my essay, "Absolute Norms in Moral Theology," in *Norm*

and Context in Christian Ethics, ed. Paul Ramsey and Gene Outka (New York: Charles Scribner's Sons, 1968).

65. This paragraph will also summarize the conclusions of the essay mentioned in note 64.

66. *I-II*, q.94, a.4

67. *In I. Sent.*, d.47, a.4. Also *De Malo*, q.3, a.1 ad17; *Quodlibetum*, I a.18.

68. Paul Elmen, Presidential Address to the American Society of Christian Ethics, 1966. Law indicates what is generally true, but miracle shows the need for exceptions to the general law.

69. Jacques Jullien, "Nature et culture: Droit naturel ou droit culturel?" *Supplément de la Vie Spirituelle*, 78 (1966), 482-502.

70. Columba Ryan, O.P., "The Traditional Concept of Natural Law: An Interpretation," in *Light on the Natural Law*, ed. Illtud Evans, O.P., (Baltimore: Helicon Press, 1965), p. 33.

71. R. Paniker, *El concepto de naturaleza: Analysis historico y metafisico di un concepto* (Madrid: Instituto Luis Vives de Filosofia, 1951); Delhaye, pp. 9-21; *Supplément de la Vie Spirituelle*, 81 (1967); 251-268; 282-322.

72. Thomas E. Davitt, S.J., *The Nature of Law* (St. Louis: B. Herder, 1951); Edouard Hamel, S.J., "La vertu d'epikie," *Sciences Ecclésiastiques*, 13 (1961), 35-56; Joseph Fuchs, S.J., "Auctoritas Dei in auctoritate civili," *Periodica de Re Morali, Canonica, Liturgica*, 52 (1963), 3-18; Gregory Stevens, O.S.B., "Moral Obligation in St. Thomas," *The Modern Schoolman*, 40 (1962-63), 1-21; M. Huftier, "La loi ecclésiastique: Sa valeur et son obligation," *L'Ami du Clergé*, 74 (1964), 375-382.

73. Such an admission is made even by the respected Thomistic scholar Jacques Maritain in *The Rights of Man and Natural Law* (New York: Charles Scribner's Sons, 1943), p. 62.

74. John C. Bennett, "Capitalism and Ethics," *Catholic Mind*, 65 (May, 1967), 44. "Though there are some differences of methodology, I am aware of no distinctive Protestant position now that can be contrasted with the economic ethics reflected in the social encylicals of Pope Pius XI and Pope John XXIII."

75. Emil Brunner, *The Divine Imperative* (Philadelphia: Westminster Press, 1947), pp. 291-562.

76. Dietrich Bonhoeffer, *Ethics* (New York: Macmillan, 1962), pp. 73-140.

77. Reinhold Niebuhr, *An Interpretation of Christian Ethics* (New York: Harper, 1935); *The Nature and Destiny of Man*, Volumes I and II (New York: Charles Scribner's Sons, original editions 1941 and 1943; paperback editions 1963); *Christian Realism and Political Problems* (New York: Charles Scribner's

Sons, 1953), especially chapter 10 on "Love and Law in Protestantism and Catholicism."

78. John C. Bennett, *Christian Ethics and Social Policy* (New York: Charles Scribner's Sons, 1950), especially pp. 116-124; Bennett, "Principles and the Context," in *Storm over Ethics* (No plave given: United Church Press, 1967), 1-25; Bennett, *Christian Social Ethics in a Changing World,* ed. John C. Bennett (New York: Association Press, 1966), pp. 369-381.

79. Paul Ramsey, *Nine Modern Moralists* (Englewood Cliffs, New Jersey: Prentice-Hall, 1962), pp. 1-8; Ramsey, *Deeds and Rules in Christian Ethics* (New York: Charles Scribner's Sons, 1967), especially p. 121, 122.

80. James M. Gustafson, "Context versus Principles: A Misplaced Debate in Christian Ethics," *Harvard Theological Review,* 58 (1965), 171-202.

81. See *Das Naturrecht im Disput,* ed. Franz Bockle (Dusseldorf: Patmos, 1966); William A. Luijpen, *Phenomenology of Natural Law* (Pittsburgh: Duquesne University Press, 1966).

82. Perhaps the most synthetic explanation of Johann's thought on the particular question of natural law is found in an unpublished address given by him to the American Society of Christian Ethics, January, 1965. Also see, Robert O. Johann, "Responsible Parenthood: A Philosophical View," *Proceedings of the Catholic Theological Society of America,* 20 (1965), 115-128; Johann, "Love and Justice," in *Ethics and Society,* ed. R. T. DeGeorge (New York: Doubleday, 1966), p. 33 ff.

83. W. van der Marck, O.P., pp. 35-63.

84. Francis Simons, "The Catholic Church and the New Morality," *Cross Currents,* 16 (1966), 429-445.

85. John G. Milhaven, S.J., "Towards an Epistemology of Ethics," *Theological Studies,* 27 (1966), 228-241.

* SELECTED BIBLIOGRAPHY

Baum, Gregory, and others, *The New Morality*. New York: Herder & Herder, 1967

Bockle, Franz *Law and Conscience*. New York: Sheed & Ward, 1966.

Bonhoeffer, Dietrich, *Ethics*. New York: Macmillan, 1965.

Curran, Charles E., *Christian Morality Today*. Notre Dame, Ind.: Fides, 1966.

——————, *A New Look at Christian Morality*. Notre Dame, Ind.: Fides, 1968.

Fletcher, Joseph, *Morals and Medicine*. Boston: Beacon, 1960.

——————, *Situation Ethics*. Philadelphia: Westminster, 1966.

——————, *Moral Responsibility*. Philadelphia: Westminster, 1967.

Fletcher, Joseph, and Thomas Wassmer, *Hello, Lovers!: An Invitation to Situation Ethics*. Washington: Corpus Books, 1970.

McDonough, Enda (ed.), *Moral Theology Renewed*. Dublin: Gill, 1965.

Monden, Louis, *Sin, Liberty and the Law*. New York: Sheed & Ward, 1965.

Wassmer, Thomas, *Christian Ethics for Today*. Milwaukee: Bruce, 1969.